PhonicsWorks™
Activity Book Advanced

Book Staff and Contributors

Kristen Kinney   *Director, Primary Literacy*
Lenna King, Amy Rauen   *Instructional Designers*
Mary Beck Desmond   *Senior Text Editor*
Jill Tunick   *Text Editor*
Suzanne Montazer   *Creative Director, Print and ePublishing*
Jayoung Cho   *Senior Print Visual Designer*
Jacqueline E.P. Rosenborough   *Print Visual Designer*
Kim Barcas, Stephanie Shaw Williams   *Cover Designers*
Amy Eward   *Senior Manager, Writers*
Susan Raley   *Senior Manager, Editors*
Deanna Lacek   *Project Manager*

Maria Szalay   *Executive Vice President, Product Development*
John Holdren   *Senior Vice President, Content and Curriculum*
David Pelizzari   *Vice President, Content and Curriculum*
Kim Barcas   *Vice President, Creative*
Laura Seuschek   *Vice President, Instructional Design, Evaluation & Studies*
Aaron Hall   *Vice President, Program Management*

Lisa Dimaio Iekel   *Senior Production Manager*

Illustrations Credits
All illustrations © K12 unless otherwise noted

About K12 Inc.
K12 Inc., a technology-based education company, is the nation's leading provider of proprietary curriculum and online education programs to students in grades K–12. K[12] provides its curriculum and academic services to online schools, traditional classrooms, blended school programs, and directly to families. K12 Inc. also operates the K[12] International Academy, an accredited, diploma-granting online private school serving students worldwide. K[12]'s mission is to provide any child the curriculum and tools to maximize success in life, regardless of geographic, financial, or demographic circumstances. K12 Inc. is accredited by CITA. More information can be found at www.K12.com.

978-1-60153-147-6
Printed by RR Donnelley, Roanoke, VA, USA, April 2012, Lot 042012

Contents

Introduce Ending Consonant Blend –mp

The Amazing Alphabet

Circle the letters that make the ending sounds in the picture name. Write the letters. Say the name.

1.  lp   mp   _____

2.  lk   mp   _____

3.  mp   lp   _____

4.  lt   mp   _____

PHONICS

Introduce Ending Consonant Blend –sp

Dissect It

Draw a square around the ending blend. Circle the vowel.
Then read the sentence aloud.

1. b (u) [m p]   Did you bump the lamp?

2. g a s p   I gasp when I run.

3. a s p   An asp can hiss.

4. w i s p   I felt a wisp of wind.

5. l i f t   Can you lift the bed?

Ending Consonant Blend –sk

The Amazing Alphabet

Circle the letters that make the ending sounds in the picture name. Write the letters in the box. Say the name.

1.    ck   sk

2.    sk   st

3.    mp   sk

4.    sk   mp

PHONICS

Ending Consonant Blend —nt
Sorting Day

Color the words that name things yellow.
Color the words that name ways to speak pink.

tell	hint	tent	mask
chant	desk	vest	ask
yell	chest	quilt	nest

Beginning Consonant Blend *bl–*
Word Parts

Underline the beginning consonant blend. Circle the vowel.
Then read the sentence aloud.

1. b l (a) c k   The cub is black.

2. b l a s t   His jet will blast off.

3. b l e n d   Blend the milk with the eggs.

4. b l o c k   We must both block him.

5. b l u f f   They went to the top of the bluff.

6. b l i m p   The blimp went up.

Beginning Consonant Blends *fl–* and *gl–*
Make Connections

Draw a line to connect the beginning and ending sounds to make a word. Write the word.

Beginning Sound	Ending Sound	
1. gl	ack	**glad**
2. bl	ug	_____
3. fl	ad	_____
4. fl	us	_____
5. pl	ip	_____
6. pl	ap	_____
7. pl	ant	_____

Beginning Consonant Blend *br–*
Careful Counting

Count the number of sounds in the word and
write the number.

Examples: chip = 3   dock = 3   vest = 4   bless = 4   crunch = 5

PHONICS

1. bat _____

2. brick _____

3. tent _____

4. ask _____

5. blimp _____

6. bran _____

7. brat _____

8. ship _____

9. brim _____

10. sand _____

11. chimp _____

12. cluck _____

13. brush _____

14. brand _____

Beginning Consonant Blends *fr–* and *gr–*

Finish the Job

Choose a word from the box to complete the sentence.
Write the word. Read the sentence aloud.

grin	frills	frog
grass	grill	fresh

1. Dad wants to _____ hot dogs.

2. Fred has a pet _____ .

3. Did Greg _____ at you?

4. I have red _____ on my dress.

5. The bug is on the _____ .

6. I smell _____-cut grass.

Introduce Beginning Digraph Blend *shr–*
Match It

Draw a line from the sentence to the matching picture.

1. The nest is in the shrub down there.

2. I like shrimp after all.

3. I know my pet has a shrill call.

Introduce Beginning Digraph Blend *thr*–
Finish the Job

Choose a word from the box to complete the sentence.
Write the word. Read the sentence aloud.

throbs	thrush	thrill

1. Fun Land was a _____ .

2. The gash on his leg _____ .

3. The _____ sits in a nest.

PHONICS

Beginning Consonant Blends *sc–* and *sp–*
Match It

Draw a line from the sentence to the matching picture.

1. The top can spin.

2. There are spots
on the spuds.

3. Did Father spend
his cash?

4. Scott has a scab
on his leg.

Beginning Consonant Blends *sk–* and *sm–*

Match It

Draw a line from the sentence to the matching picture.

1. Smack the pup is small.

2. The swan can swim.

3. The skunk has a bad smell.

4. I will skip and jump.

PHONICS

Beginning Consonant Blend *spr–*
Dissect It

Find the word that begins with *spr–* in the sentence.
Write the word.

1. I can run fast. I can sprint.   **sprint** _____

2. Go pick a sprig.   _____

3. Did Jack Sprat like fat?   _____

4. Is Miss Sprizz French?   _____

5. I can write to Trish Spriss.   _____

PHONICS

Beginning Consonant Blends *squ–* and *scr–*
Hunt for Information

Choose a word from the story that completes the sentence.
Write the word.

A squid has ten legs and two fins. Its skin has a red tint. Many squid are just one inch. Others get to be very grand. Some can swim fast, others just drift. A squid hunts for fish. It stretches out its legs. Then it straps them onto the fish to kill it.

1. A _____**squid**_____ has ten legs and two fins.

2. Its _____ is red.

3. Some squid are just one _____ .

4. Some squid can _____ fast.

5. It _____ its legs onto a fish to kill it.

Words Ending in –ank
Match It

Draw a line to match the words that begin with the same letter.

1. bank   raft

2. drank   truck

3. Frank   blank

4. rank   yes

5. sank   dress

6. tank   frost

7. yank   sack

Words Ending in –*onk* and –*unk*

To the Rescue

Help the rabbit find the path to the log.
Color the boxes that name real words.

honk	nink	lonk
junk	pink	sunk
kull	dup	junk
epp	drink	stink
kimp	dunk	thag
tilk	ink	zank

Words Ending in –ang
Go Fish!

Color fish with the sound /ang/ yellow.
Color fish with the sound /ank/ pink.

sang

bank

fang

hang

rank

gang

Words Ending in –*ong* and –*ung*

Best Pick

Read the sentence aloud and circle the word that best completes it. Then write the word.

1. She loves to sing a _____ .

2. An inch is not so _____ .

3. She _____ up the wet cloth.

4. Will the bell _____ ?

sung   song

long   lung

hang   hung

thing   ring

Silent *e* Spelling for Sound /ā/
Alphabet Addition

Add the letters to make a word. Write the word, and then read it aloud.

1. cap + e = _____ **cape** _____

2. can + e = _____

3. mat + e = _____

4. fat + e = _____

5. rat + e = _____

6. Sam + e = _____

 Just for Fun

Read the sentence aloud.

Kate made pink capes for Kim and Jane.

PHONICS

Silent *e* Spelling for Sound /ō/
Finish the Job

Choose a word from the box to complete the sentence.
Write the word. Read the sentence aloud.

> time   hope   miles
>
> robe   vase   plate

1. I rode my bike for five _____.

2. Put the rose in a _____.

3. For the first _____, I can skate fast.

4. Did you put the cake on this _____?

5. The king had a red _____.

6. I _____ the plane is on time.

Introduce Silent *e* Spelling for Sound /ū/
Alphabet Addition

Add the letters to make a word. Write the word, and then read it aloud.

1. cut   +   e   =   _____cute_____

2. fus   +   e   =   _____

3. mul   +   e   =   _____

4. cub   +   e   =   _____

 Just for Fun ....

Read the silly sentence aloud.

Did a mule bake a cake with a cube of grass?

Introduce Silent *e* Spelling for Long Double *o* Sound

Fun with Long Double *o* Sound

Read the word aloud. Read the sentence aloud, and then circle the word with the sound /o͞o/ in it. Read the sentence again.

1. plume   I see a (plume) of smoke.

2. June   It gets so hot in June.

3. tune   None of them sang a tune.

4. tube   Put your tube in the water.

5. flute   I have a drum and she has a flute.

6. dune   See! That is a tall sand dune.

7. rude   It is rude to stare at people.

PHONICS

Introduce Sounds /ar/ and /or/

Match It

Draw a line from the sentence to the matching picture.

1. The dogs bark in the park.

2. Sharks have a sharp bite.

3. The corn is on the fork.

4. The acorn is on the porch.

Review Beginning Blends

Match It

Draw a line from the sentence to the matching picture.

1. The bells will start to ring.

2. I will swing for a short time.

3. It is smart to keep things in a trunk.

4. Did you get the pen?

PHONICS

Contractions

Alphabet Subtraction

Read the two words aloud, and then write them as one contraction. (Where the o should be, write an apostrophe.)

1. is not   —   o   =   __isn't__

2. did not   —   o   =   _____

3. are not   —   o   =   _____

4. has not   —   o   =   _____

5. was not   —   o   =   _____

6. can not   —   no   =   _____

PHONICS

Practice Contractions and Sound /z/ Spelled *s* (A)

Best Pick

Read the sentence aloud and circle the word that best completes it. Then write the word.

1. The mule _____ want to go.

2. The cats _____ together.

3. Let's _____ the kite.

4. She _____ gone home yet.

5. They didn't _____ to go there.

6. He didn't _____ his chopsticks.

wasn't	didn't
aren't	can't
chase	cute
isn't	hasn't
want	went
use	us

PHONICS

Introduce Two-Syllable Words
Careful Counting

Count how many syllables you hear in the word and write the number.

1. hope _____

2. picnic _____

3. basketball _____

4. pumpkin _____

5. rabbit _____

6. insect _____

7. rake _____

8. stack _____

9. velvet _____

10. kittens _____

11. tent _____

12. lemonade _____

13. muffins _____

14. admit _____

15. fantastic _____

16. napkin _____

PHONICS

Introduce Schwa Sound
Match It

Draw a line from the sentence to the matching picture.

1. Some of the pumpkins are ripe.

2. Mr. Barton has a kitten.

3. I have a rabbit.

4. It will all fit in the picnic basket.

5. I will rest after I hit the target.

6. The insects ate after the storm.

Introduce Endings –*ing* and –*est*
Alphabet Addition

Add the letters to make a word. Write the word, and then read it aloud.

1. run + n + ing = __running__

2. hop + p + ing = _____

3. nap + p + ing = _____

4. pin + n + ing = _____

5. hug + g + ing = _____

6. skip + p + ing = _____

7. bat + t + ing = _____

 Just for Fun

Read the sentence aloud.

They are hopping and skipping.

Where is he pinning the flag?

Introduce Ending –ed
Practice What You Know

Read the word aloud. Then, rewrite the word, adding the endings –ed and –ing. Read the words you wrote aloud.

Base Word	Add –ed	Add –ing
1. land	landed	landing
2. jump	_____	_____
3. park	_____	_____
4. happen	_____	_____
5. sort	_____	_____
6. twist	_____	_____
7. trust	_____	_____

Introduce Consonant Ending –le
Alphabet Addition

Add the letters to make a word. Write the word, and then read it aloud.

1. ap + ple = __apple__

2. can + dle = _____

3. pud + dle = _____

4. bun + dle = _____

5. bub + ble = _____

6. puz + zle = _____

7. lit + tle = _____

Introduce Digraph *ph*

Match It

Draw a line from the sentence to the matching picture.

1. The kettle is on the table.

2. Ladle the punch into my cup.

3. Tell me a fable about a turtle.

4. I saw a black jacket.

5. Phil likes to do puzzles.

6. My uncle is on the phone.

Sound /s/ Spelled c

Careful Counting

Count how many syllables you hear in the word and write the number.

1. race _____

2. bracelet _____

3. pencil _____

4. icebox _____

5. trace _____

6. Bruce _____

7. playmate _____

8. convince _____

9. spice _____

10. racetrack _____

11. since _____

12. placement _____

13. rice _____

14. sentence _____

PHONICS

Sound /j/ Spelled –dge
Finish the Job

Choose a word from the box to complete the sentence.
Write the word. Read the sentence aloud.

badge	working	slice
small	mice	edge

1. The judge is _____ at his bench.

2. We have very _____ cells inside us.

3. The fire marshall has a _____.

4. The _____ ate my _____ of cake!

5. Face west; see the _____ of the setting sun.

Introduce Spellings for Sound /ā/
Investigator

Read each word aloud, going down each column.
Then read each word again, going across each row.

a–e	ai	ay	eigh	a
lace	rain	play	eight	acorn
plate	chain	way	weight	David
made	train	say	weigh	raven
tape	brain	stay	sleigh	label
page	sail	day	freight	data
snake	paint	spray	neigh	major
lane	main	pay		fable
cane	braid	tray		basic
place	pail	May		April
grape	faint	gray		bacon

Circle the answer.

1. Where do you see *ai* in words?   middle   end

2. Where do you see *ay* in words?   middle   end

3. Which spelling has more words?   *ai*   *eigh*

Practice Spellings for Sound /ā/ (B)

Investigator

Read each word aloud. Write the word in the correct column.

main	wait	say	Spain
gray	drain	faint	play
way	may	braid	today

Long _a_ Sound in the Middle of the Word	**Long _a_ Sound at the End of the Word**
1. **main**	7. **say**
2. _____	8. _____
3. _____	9. _____
4. _____	10. _____
5. _____	11. _____
6. _____	12. _____

PHONICS

Introduce Spellings for Sound /ī/
Investigator

Read down each column, and then read across each row.

i–e	igh	i	y	ie
dine	sigh	hi	fly	tie
hive	light	wild	cry	pie
prize	sight	child	shy	die
size	night	mild	try	lie
kite	might	kind	dry	fie
pile	fight	find	fry	
line	fright	mind	spy	
bike	lightning	behind	why	
spike	right	title	my	

Circle the answer.

1. What letter usually follows *igh*?   *t*   *b*

2. Where is *y* in these words?   middle   end

3. Where is *ie* in these words?   middle   end

Practice Spellings for Sound /ī/ (B)
Finish the Job

Choose a word from the box to complete the sentence.
Write the word. Read the sentence aloud.

bright	fight	child
sight	might	sign

1. The _____ said, "Stop."

2. A sunrise is a splendid _____.

3. Why did the cats begin to _____?

4. Let's get away from the _____ lights.

5. The nice _____ has gone to help.

6. Mom _____ bake a pie tonight.

Introduce Spellings for Sound /ō/

Investigator

Read down each column, and then read across each row.

o-e	oa	ow	oe	o
home	boat	row	toe	go
joke	float	tow	doe	so
rope	boast	snow	hoe	both
scope	coal	grow	woe	old
stone	croak	show	oboe	fold
pole	road	flow	foe	cold
alone	goat	bow		most
phone	throat	glow		sold
cone	soak	slow		told

Circle the answer.

1. Where is *ow* in these words?   middle   end

2. Where is *oa* in these words?   middle   end

PHONICS

Practice Spellings for Sound /ō/ (B)
Tic Tac Toe

Read each word aloud. Find the five words in a row that rhyme. The row can be across, down, or diagonal. Color the five boxes that contain the five rhyming words.

go	so	hope	tote	coat
oak	foe	rope	float	doe
croak	yoke	goat	most	toe
soak	throat	moat	toast	hoe
oat	gold	sold	fold	glow

Introduce Spellings for Sound /ē/

Investigator

Read down each column and then read across each row.

e	ea	ee	e–e	ie	y
me	sea	see	eve	chief	candy
be	tea	bee	Pete	thief	sixty
she	pea	feed	extreme	grief	rusty
hero	eat	meet	complete	brief	sassy
feline	leak	need	here	yield	bunny
zero	weak	keen	athlete	shield	lucky
rewind	cream	feet	delete	field	happy
eject	meat	teeth	trapeze	piece	jelly
behind	beans	bleed	adhere	niece	tardy
elastic	each	speech			baby
begin	heat	cheese			lady

Circle the answer.

1. Where is *y* in these words?   middle   end

Write the correct answers.

2. Which letters can spell the sound /ē/ in the middle of a word? _____

Practice Spellings for Sound /ē/ (B)

Tic Tac Toe

Read each word aloud. Find the five words in a row that rhyme. The row can be across, down, or diagonal. Color the five boxes that contain the five rhyming words.

tree	flea	bee	each	holly
three	see	glee	peach	jolly
sea	sheep	peep	teach	dear
dream	weep	thief	reach	Polly
steep	deep	Pete	beach	dolly

Introduce Spellings for Sound /ū/

Investigator

Read down each column, and then read across each row.

u–e	u	ue
cube	music	hue
use	cupid	argue
mule	menu	rescue
cute	human	value
fume	bugle	continue
fuse	unicorn	
	unite	
	united	
	humid	

Circle the answer.

1. Where is *ue* in these words? middle end

Practice Spellings for Sounds /ū/ and Long Double o (A)

Rhyming Words

Read the pair of words aloud. Do the words rhyme?
Write *Y* for Yes or *N* for No.

			Yes	**No**
1.	cool	pool	Y	
2.	cute	rude		N
3.	rude	dude		
4.	true	blue		
5.	tooth	boost		
6.	human	humid		
7.	broom	room		
8.	Ruth	truth		

Introduce Spellings for Short Double *o* Sound

Investigator

Circle the words with the sound /o͝o/, as in *book*, yellow.
Circle the words with the sound /o͞o/, as in *moon*, pink.

(book)	nook	(moon)	took
brook	cook	shook	food
good	broom	stood	crook
boot	hoof	wood	wooden
look	foot	wool	hook
balloon	hood	football	raccoon

Circle the answer.

1. Where is oo in these words?   middle   end

Practice Spellings for Long Double *o* Sound (B)

Clues

Read the clue aloud. Find the word in the box that matches the clue, and write it next to the clue.

notebook	cookbook
hook	football
hood	shook

Clue	What Is It?
1. Used for catching fish	_____
2. Used to play game	_____
3. Used for taking notes	_____
4. Trembled and quaked	_____
5. Part of some coats	_____
6. Tells how to prepare foods	_____

Review Long Vowels and Double *o* Sounds (A)

Hunt for Information

Choose a word from the story that completes the sentence.
Write the word.

> A kangaroo is a mammal. On each of its back legs is a very big foot. The smallest kangaroo is called a wallaby. The largest is the red kangaroo. 'Roos can hop over forty miles in one hour. They can leap over a ten-foot fence.
>
> Kangaroos rest in the shade in the afternoon. They come out to eat late in the day when it gets cool. They eat grass for food. Kangaroos can go without water for a few months.

1. A _____ is a mammal with two big feet.

2. 'Roos can hop _____.

3. Kangaroos rest in the _____.

4. They come out to eat when it is _____.

Review Long Vowels and Double *o* Sounds (C)

By Sight

Reading across the rows, see how many words you can read correctly in one minute. When you get to the bottom of the page, start over.

saw	about	behind	now	move
follow	come	neighbor	against	here
please	once	every	these	above
now	about	saw	move	behind
against	here	come	follow	please

Introduce Sound /er/ Spelled –er, –ir, –ur, and –ear

Many Spellings for One Sound

Look for the spelling pattern in the word that spells the sound /er/. Write *er, ir, ur,* or *ear* after the word.

1. fern   **er** _____

2. earth   _____

3. turn   _____

4. burp   _____

5. third   _____

6. her   _____

7. sir   _____

8. fir   _____

9. fur   _____

10. learn _____

11. shirt _____

12. hurt   _____

13. curl   _____

14. jerk   _____

15. earn   _____

16. skirt _____

17. surf   _____

18. germ   _____

PHONICS

Practice Sound /er/ Spelled –er, –ir, –ur, and –ear, (B)

Identification, Please

Read across the row aloud. Color the words that have the sound /er/, as in *her*, *girl*, *burn*, and *earth*, yellow.

thunder	dirt	platter	corner
fear	cider	rule	earth
surprise	third	circle	bird
bride	near	cooler	badger
hurry	heard	finger	dear
person	stir	clear	furry

Introduce Sound /ĕ/ Spelled *ea*
Pick the Word

Read the sentence. Find the word that has the sound /ĕ/ as in *bread*. Write the word.

1. We ate too much bread. **bread**

2. This thread is perfect for my skirt. _____

3. Will you be my partner instead? _____

4. I have a blue feather. _____

5. I ate after I read my book. _____

6. She dealt five cards to each player. _____

7. I don't know if she is ready. _____

Practice Sound /ĕ/ Spelled *ea* (B)

Hunt for Information

Highlight words that have the sound /ĕ/ spelled *ea* as in *bread*. Choose a word from the story that completes the sentence. Write the word.

The Golden Pheasant is kept on many bird farms. It is easy to raise these birds. They stay healthy for a long time. The male has a bright golden breast and feathers. The female has a dull brown breast and feathers. Pheasants like to eat corn, grain, chopped apples, peanuts, crickets, and earthworms.

1. A pheasant is a kind of _____.

2. The Golden _____ is kept on many farms.

3. The pheasant stays _____ for a long time.

4. The male has a golden _____ and feathers.

5. The female has a brown breast and _____.

Introduce Sound /oi/ Spelled *oi* and *oy*
Investigator

Read each word aloud. Write the word in the correct column.

joy	coin	boy	noise
point	join	toy	joint
boil	ahoy	Roy	Troy

oy	*oi*

Practice Sound /oi/ Spelled *oi* and *oy* (B)
Sentence Spree

Read the sentence aloud. Highlight each word that has the
sound /oi/, as in *boy* or *coin*.

1. Roy is such a pleasant little boy.

2. They enjoyed their new toys so much.

3. I know that noise will annoy Father.

4. They will join us after the show.

5. After the water boils, we will put in the eggs.

6. Do you think the bread will spoil?

7. I have only one coin in my pocket.

8. Only one pencil has a sharp point.

Introduce Sound /aw/ Spelled *au* and *aw*

Investigator

Read each word aloud. Write the word in the correct column.

paw	pause	lawn	Paul
draw	straw	laundry	August
fawn	faucet		

aw	*au*

Practice Sound /aw/ Spelled *au* and *aw* (B)

Alphabet Addition

Add the letters to make a word. Write the word, and then read it aloud.

1. jaw   +   bone   =   **jawbone**

2. cole   +   slaw   =   _____

3. be   +   cause   =   _____

4. aw   +   ful   =   _____

5. law   +   yer   =   _____

6. squawk   +   ing   =   _____

7. draw   +   ing   =   _____

Introduce Sound /ow/ Spelled *ou* and *ow*

Investigator

Read each word aloud. Write the word in the correct column.

trout	flower	around	shower
pound	frown	powder	cloud
cow	sour	found	down

ow	*ou*

PHONICS

Practice Sound /ow/ Spelled *ou* and *ow* (B)
By Sight

Reading across the rows, see how many words you can read correctly in one minute. When you get to the bottom of the page, start over.

children	nothing	everything	please	once
every	these	against	now	behind
about	saw	whether	over	number
write	almost	under	follow	come
neighbor	children	number	now	write

Introduce Sound /ō/ Spelled *ow*

Investigator

Read the word aloud and listen to the sound that the *ow* in that word makes. Write the word in the correct column.

howl	own	flow	wow
towel	town	bowling	pillow
fellow	window	brown	tower

ow as in *cow*   *ow* as in *grow*

1. _____   7. _____

2. _____   8. _____

3. _____   9. _____

4. _____   10. _____

5. _____   11. _____

6. _____   12. _____

Practice Sound /ō/ Spelled *ow* (B)

Finish the Job

Choose a word from the box to complete the sentence.
Write the word. Read the sentence aloud.

> flowers   snowman   towel
>
> clown   marshmallows   now

1. After my bath, I need a _____ to dry off.

2. In winter, we make a _____ outside.

3. Mom said, "I want you to come inside _____."

4. Those _____ make our yard colorful.

5. I like to roast _____ on a campfire.

6. The funny_____ at the circus has a big red nose.

PHONICS